Hawaiian Massage ⋮ Lomilomi

Text by R. Makana Risser Chai

Photographs by John C. Kalani Zak

Hawaiian Massage : Lomilomi

sacred touch of aloha

Hawaiian Insights, Inc. Kailua, Hawai'i

Authors' Note: The Hawaiian people, both historically and today, have great diversity in their practices, traditions, and beliefs. This book recounts oral histories from the Bishop Museum, writings by early visitors, research by Native Hawaiian scholars, and personal interviews. There are many wonderful teachers and practitioners in the Hawaiian Islands and around the world. The people pictured in this book are just a few we have been honored to meet.

It is always good to be reminded of the Hawaiian proverb, "All wisdom is not taught in one school." Each practitioner is different. They may not all agree with all the views expressed in this book. It is our intention to honor all authentic lomilomi traditions.

While every effort has been made to be accurate and respectful, there may be errors or omissions. Please let us know of any way this book can be improved by writing to Aloha@HawaiianInsights.com. Mahalo.

Legal Notice: This book is not a how-to manual. Lomilomi can be learned only from a teacher, not a book. Physical manipulations described here may be dangerous if performed by the untrained. Nothing in this book is meant to be medical advice. If you are ill, contact a health care professional immediately. The authors and publisher do not recommend any particular lomilomi practitioner, do not warrant any practitioner's performance, have no knowledge if any is licensed and insured, and disclaim any and all liability for claimed harm from any practitioner listed in this book.

Hawaiian Massage — Lomilomi:
Sacred Touch of Aloha
by R. Makana Risser Chai
and John C. Kalani Zak
Hawaiian Insights, Inc.

ISBN 978-0-9791867-0-7

Separation, Printing & Binding
in EBS Editoriale Bortolazzi-Stey - Italy
October 2007
9 8 7 6 5 4 3 2

Design by Jim Wageman, Wigwag

Hawaiian Insights, Inc.
P.O. Box 1835, Kailua, Hawai'i 96734
Phone 808-282-2743
Fax 808-263-5929
aloha@HawaiianInsights.com
www.HawaiianInsights.com

Makana's Dedication

For my mother,
Doris Risser Kalenda,
who first inspired
my love of Hawai'i.

John's Dedication

To my parents, Edwin and Juanita Zak,
who, without even realizing it,
brought me home to Hawai'i;
and to Darlene Conley,
who taught me to live vibrantly.

Contents

Mahalo, Mahalo, Mahalo

Mahalo, thank you, to all who made this book possible. Mahalo ke Akua. Mahalo to the *kūpuna* (elders), *kumu* (teachers), and *kānaka lomi* (practitioners) whose words and pictures are here. Mahalo to the friends and family who modeled for the photographs and helped us to publish. Mahalo to all lomilomi practitioners who keep the tradition alive, and to every person who perpetuates lomilomi by receiving it. Mahalo to the Hawaiian people who preserved the culture and traditions of their ancestors. Mahalo to the ancestors.

Mahalo to kumu lomi Brenda Mohalapua Ignacio. She introduced us to each other and to many of the people in this book. She made many phone calls, traveled with us, encouraged us, and most importantly, made us laugh. Her spirit infuses this book.

Mahalo to the kumu and kānaka lomi whose *kōkua* (assistance) made this book possible:

Allen Elia Keala Alapaʻi
Antoinette Kahili Alapaʻi
Alva James Andrews
Henry Auwae
Noelani Bennett

Kaliko Chang
Keala Ching
Mary Fragas
Kawaikapuokalani Hewett
Haunani Hopkins
Mana Hopkins
Brenda Mohalapua Ignacio
Donald Kaiahua
Kalua Kaiahua
Parker Kaipo Kaneakua
Abraham Kawaiʻi
Hoʻokahi Kawaiʻi Hoʻoulu
Jeanella Keopuhiwa
Kehaulani Keopuhiwa
Sylvester "Papa K" Kepilino
Koni
Angeline Locey
Malia Locey
Michael Locey
Margaret Machado
Nerita Machado
Judson Kealohakeikihipa McCandless
Maikaʻi Medeiros
Jeana Iwalani Naluai
Kamaile Puaoi
Henry Kaleiwohi "Butch" Richards
Kamehanaokala Ruiz
Wesley Waianiani Sen
Dane Kaohelani Silva
Ramsay Taum
Li Ann Uyeda
Eri Mahealani Sakai Virden
Aoi Wright

Mahalo to the people in this book,
our 'ohana, our lomilomi family.

Hawaiian Massage Lomilomi

The Touch of Aloha ⋮ **Lomilomi**

Hawai'i is unique because of the aloha of the Hawaiian people.
Aloha means love, caring, and compassion. One way Hawaiians
share their aloha is through lomilomi (lo-mi-lo-mi).

Haunani gently pulls and stretches the neck through a complete range of motion, relaxing Eri's entire body.

Sometimes called Hawaiian massage, lomilomi is much more than massage. Lomilomi aligns the body, mind, heart, and spirit through loving touch. It is ancient, but still practiced by native healers in community health centers, for the finest spas, and at the best hotels in Hawai'i and around the world.

As Eri drifts away to the sound
of the waves softly breaking on
the shore, she feels nurtured and
supported in Haunani's hands.

"One practice, which has survived to this day, called lomilomi,
is a luxurious one. It is a process in which skillful natives knead
the body with their hands, and manipulate the joints, after which
a delightful and refreshing languor steals over the whole body."

ALEXANDER S. TWOMBLY, 1900

Sacred *kalo* (taro) growing in
Waiāhole on Oʻahu. The *poi* made
from kalo is the most important
food of the Hawaiians, both
physically and spiritually.

The peoples of ancient Egypt, Greece, India, China, and Japan practiced massage. The voyagers from the South Pacific who first discovered Hawaiʻi more than 1500 years ago brought massage with them, just as they brought food staples, farm animals, and medicinal herbs. Once they settled the land, their massage techniques changed and evolved to become uniquely Hawaiian. As an indigenous practice, lomilomi varied by island, by ahupuaʻa *(district running from the mountains to the sea), and by* ʻohana *(family).*

One of the first European artists to
visit Hawai'i, Ukrainian Louis Choris
painted this watercolor from his
1816 drawing. It shows an *ali'i*
(chief) surrounded by his retinue.
Perhaps the servant whose hands
we can't see is giving lomilomi.

Traditionally, everyone in the 'ohana knew lomilomi and massaged each other every day. Native healers used it as physical therapy to cure injury and illness. Servants gave lomilomi to the ali'i, *the chiefly class, as a luxury of life. The chiefs' "common position was reclining upon divans of fine mats, surrounded by a retinue, devoted solely to their physical gratification. Some fanned, brushed away insects and held spittoons; others fed them, lomi-lomied, or dressed their hair or persons."* JAMES JACKSON JARVES, 1843

Love of the Land : **Aloha ʻĀina**

Previous: Palm trees on the deserted beach at Lapakahi, a traditional healing place on the island of Hawai'i.

Opposite: Sunrise at Kualoa on O'ahu, an ancient *pu'uhonua* (place of refuge) held sacred by Hawaiians.

What makes lomilomi unique? It starts with aloha 'āina, *love of the land. Hawaiians know the land itself is healing. Certain areas possess special healing powers. Hawai'i's last reigning monarch, Queen Lili'uokalani, believed in the curative effect of her land at Waikīkī, called Hamohamo (ha-mo-ha-mo). Hamohamo literally means "to massage with oil."*

The day John went to Hamohamo to take pictures for this book, this magical rainbow appeared. Despite the high rises where once stood only coconut palms, visitors from around the world still find healing here today.

"Hamohamo is justly considered to be the most life-giving and healthy district in the whole extent of the island of Oʻahu; there is something unexplainable and peculiar in the atmosphere of that place, which seldom fails to bring back the glow of health to the patient, no matter from what disease suffering."

QUEEN LILIʻUOKALANI, 1898

Just beneath the hard, cold surface of barren lava lies a sea of hot magma. Traditional Hawaiians believe the volcano goddess Pele lives here.

A*nother place associated with lomilomi is the volcano on the island of Hawai'i. In 1908, Bishop Museum Director William T. Brigham wrote, "Once I had been in the saddle all day on a slow horse traveling the then execrable trail from Hilo to the volcano of Kilauea in the rainy season. Arrived late at night at the grass house that then served to shelter visitors at the brink of the crater, I dismounted so stiff and weary that I could not sleep; I could hardly sit down. Fortunately there were then many natives living in that desolate neighborhood . . . and among them were found two old women noted for their skill. . . . [continued]*

"At first they gently kneaded the muscles from the extremity of the trunk, then tapping in succession with finger tips, knuckles and closed fists, and ending with a minuet danced on my abdomen and a march on their heels up and down my spine. I think they, in the course of this, ran their heels down every rib as if it were the key of a piano. They also 'cracked' each finger joint and even my neck; at first it was ticklish; then dreamy; then restful, and after an hour of this I got up so refreshed that I could have ridden all night. Instead I at once fell asleep." WILLIAM T. BRIGHAM, 1908

Beachboy Joe Miner circa 1935.
From about 1905 to the 1950s,
Native Hawaiian beachboys living
on Waikīkī Beach taught surfing and
gave lomilomi. Duke Kahanamoku
(1890–1968), a five-time Olympic
medal-winning swimmer, traveled
the world teaching surfing.

Lomilomi practitioners today often give treatments outdoors so patients can see the mountains, feel the warm caress of the breeze, smell the flowers, hear the waves, and taste the salt air. "Among Waikiki beachboys, it was almost as popular as surfing. David Kahanamoku, one of Duke's brothers, gave lomi lomi all his life.... The beachboys would set up a surfboard on sawhorses and use the hand and elbow method of lomi lomi." MARILYN KELLY, 1977

Dance & Martial Arts : **Hula & Lua**

Previous: Brenda Mohalapua
Ignacio greets the dawn at Lanikai.

Opposite: Her daughter-in-law, Eri,
competing in the Merrie Monarch
festival. Nine of the practitioners
in this book dance hula, notably
Kawaikapuokalani Hewett.

*Just as lomilomi springs from the earth, it also grows out of
Hawaiian culture. Many traditional practitioners infuse
their lomilomi with the moves of hula or* lua, *the martial art.
"Lomilomi is to and from the heart, taking the blood faster to
the heart. I massage to and from the arms and the legs, pushing
the blood to the heart faster, to and from. Pushing to and from,
to and from. The one-two-three is the same as they dance the
hula. Lomilomi—one two three. One two three pinch off."*

AUNTIE MARGARET MACHADO, 1999

Lua is known as the art of bone breaking. It also targets specific nerves to cause incapacitation. Lua masters have a detailed knowledge of anatomy in order to execute their moves. They practice lomilomi to correct joint injury, realign the body, and knead sore muscles after training.

Prayer : **Pule**

Previous: Haunani says, "Ke Akua God guides our hands through our hearts."

Opposite: Eri begins with prayer.

The touch of lomilomi springs from the deep spirituality of the Hawaiians. Prayer was and is an essential part of the daily lives of the Hawaiians. The old ones prayed when dancing hula, going into battle, and giving lomilomi. Native practitioners, then and now, pray before, during, and after treatment. "Lomilomi is praying work."

Papa Auwae in 1999 at the
restored sacred village of Lapakahi,
where he learned herbal medicine, *lā'au
lapa'au,* from his great-grandmother.

"Hawaiians of old 'cleared the way' with prayers before
they began an undertaking." MARY KAWENA PUKUI, 1972

"80 percent of healing is spiritual, and 20 percent lā'au."

PAPA HENRY AUWAE, 1968

Opposite: On the shores of
Kāneʻohe Bay at Heʻeia, the home
of his ancestors, Kawaikapuokalani
Hewett chants his prayer.

Below: Noelani Bennett
prays as she works.

"For healing, planting, fishing, harmony of spirit, of working of nature is essential. By recognizing this, and establishing it with prayer, reverence, silence, working in early morning and evening, the old Hawaiian believed he derived great benefit from his labor." EMMA AKANA OLMSTED, 1933

At the water's edge in urban Honolulu, Ala Moana Park may seem an unlikely place to find herbal medicine, but Kaipo Kaneakua uses endemic trees and many of the "weeds" growing in the grass.

"When a treatment is to be given, the one who gives the treatment first plucks the herbs to be used. He prays as he picks the herbs. No one should call him back or distract his attention, all should be as still as possible for they do not want the vibration broken.... They knew the laws of vibration. They knew the power of the spoken word. They knew Nature. They gathered the vibration of the plentiful."

EMMA AKANA OLMSTED, 1930

When Uncle Butch led herb walks, he often began the day at sunrise on a high peak and ended on the beach at sunset. Hawaiian medicine also uses earth, shells, salt, and seaweed.

"When we pray, we are asking for permission. We ask permission of the plants to take them. The plants are the real kānaka maoli — the first Native Hawaiians." UNCLE BUTCH RICHARDS, 2005

The people of old prayed to the gods of healing, to their family gods ('aumakua), and to Hamo'ea, the goddess of massage. "Hamoea is the principal goddess of those who practice the art of massage." JOSEPH S. EMERSON, 1918

The name "Hamo'ea" is rich with implication. One meaning is "Hamo'ea-anointed-with-oil / patroness-of-various-diseases / cure-by-massage-therapy / give-to-the-patient-the-spiritual-breath-of-life."

LUCIA TARALLO JENSEN and NATALIE MAHINA JENSEN, 2005

Auntie Margaret Machado, named a "Living Treasure of Hawai'i," became one of the first Native Hawaiians to become a licensed massage therapist, and the first known to open a school to teach non-Hawaiians.

After 1820, most Hawaiians converted to Christianity, but prayer remains an essential part of lomilomi. "In the old days, take it to the gods. Today, take it to God." MARY KAWENA PUKUI, 1972

"The Lord does the healing. I don't heal. That's why I say prayer. I ask the Lord to intervene." AUNTIE MARGARET MACHADO, 1999

LiAnn Uyeda moves energy
as she works in her "Hawaiian
Healing Hale" (Home) in Honolulu.

Some contemporary practitioners continue to pray to the old gods, especially ʻaumakua. Others have a different spiritual approach. "During a genuine lomilomi session, the therapist is aligned with divine energy, and keeps his or her heart and mind clear for spirit to move through them as a conduit for healing energy. Proper breathing and pure thoughts are important. According to the Hawaiians, thoughts contain mana, or energy. When thoughts are combined with touch and breath they are transferred to the receiver. Therefore the therapist's thoughts must be focused on love and healing." TAMARA MONDRAGON, 2000

Kahu Abraham Kawaiʻi founded Kahuna Bodywork,™ known for long, flowing strokes and fluid, rhythmic foot movements.

"There is nothing you cannot change; you are a creator. Awareness is the first step to understanding that every individual has the capability to promote better health by the way they think. Prayer is one such focused extension of thought, and can create empowerment and changes."

KAHU ABRAHAM KAWAIʻI, 1987

Navigation

Star come
Star go
Island come
Island go
Ocean come
Ocean go
Life come
Life go
I sail
I fly
I sail
I stand
Center of the universe.

KAHU ABRAHAM KAWAIʻI

Loving Touch : **Lomi Aloha**

Lomilomi is unique because it is always done with loving touch.
"Lomilomi is a loving touch, letting them feel you. When they feel
loving hands on their body, they'll respond: 'She loves me, she'll
take good care of me, and I'm going to get well.' It's your talk and
your approach. They know that you love them. Getting them to
relax their body so there'll be no stress. It's love! If your hands are
gentle and loving, your patient will feel the sincerity of your heart,
his soul will reach out to yours, and God's healing power will flow
through you both." AUNTIE MARGARET MACHADO, 1999

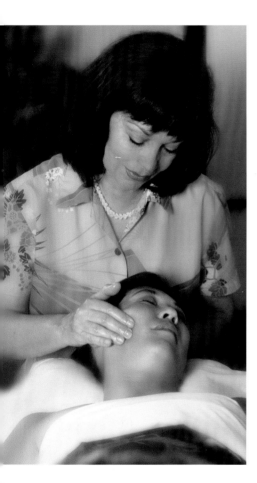
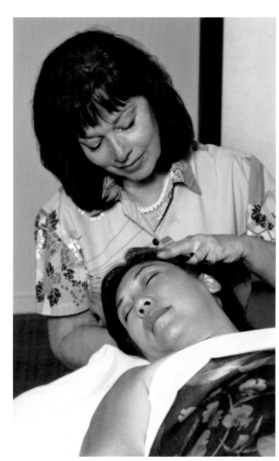
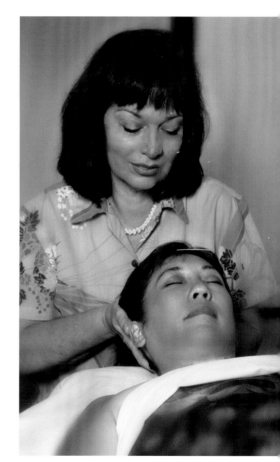

Breath ⋮ **Hā**

Papa K imparts *hā* (breath) to his grandnephew. First he works the affected part with his fingers, then cups his hands and forcefully breathes on it.

The touch of lomilomi is integrated with breath. The Hawaiian word for breath is hā. *Hā also means exhale. And since the old Hawaiians were deeply aware that without breath there is no life, hā means life. The* kāhuna *la'au lapa'au (master healers) created herbal remedies and then hā—exhaled—on them to impart mana.*

"Hawaii had long observed the connection between breathing and life. Long before the missionaries arrived, Hawaiians had invested the 'breath of life' with a spiritual significance that closely paralleled Biblical references." MARY KAWENA PUKUI, 1972

Work of the Hands : Hana Lima

Previous: The loving touch
of Nerita Machado.

Opposite: As Haunani Hopkins
gives lomilomi to Makana's
husband Mark, he faces sacred
Mōkapu Peninsula, the home
of his ancestors and one of the
earliest settlements on O'ahu.

T*he movements of the hands, combined with the power of prayer,
breath, and loving touch, are what make lomilomi unique. "It is
a gentle, graceful, rhythmic, light or deep massage to parts of the
external body's pressure points, nerve centers, muscle tissues and
internal organs. It removes toxic waste, tension, pain and fatigue,
and replaces them with positive energy, increases circulation and
improves muscle tone."* JIMMY LEWIS, 1996

Aoi Wright gives lomilomi at Moku Ola Hawaiian Healing Center, overlooking the historic fish pond of Maunalua on O'ahu where King Kamehameha the Great once worked.

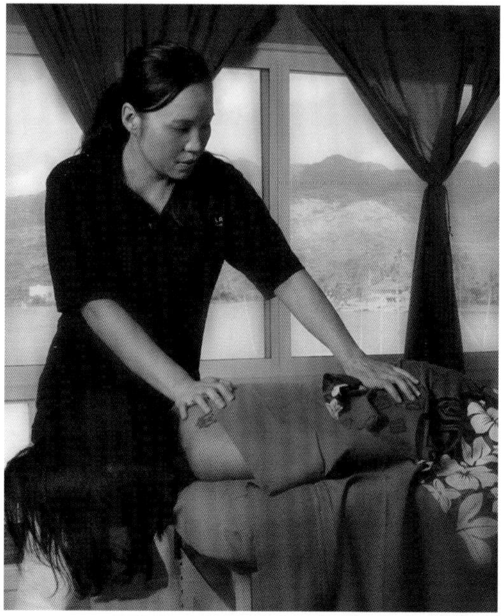

"I conceive it to be a system of deep communication using biomechanical and energetic waves to stimulate the cells to heal and regenerate. Hawaiian lomilomi consists of both gentle and deep techniques, such as rubbing and stroking, kneading, pounding, pressing, shaking, vibrating, pulling, pinching, rolling and deep pressure-point compressions. Energetic techniques that coordinate breath and spirit would normally be integrated into the manual procedures." DANE KAOHELANI SILVA, 2000

"To you thereupon comes a stout native, with soft, fleshy hands but a strong grip, and, beginning with your head and working down slowly over the whole body, seizes and squeezes with a quite peculiar art every tired muscle, working and kneading with indefatigable patience until in half an hour, whereas you were sore and weary and worn-out, you find yourself fresh, all soreness and weariness absolutely and entirely removed, and mind and body soothed to a healthful and refreshing sleep."

CHARLES NORDHOFF, 1874

On deserted Waimānalo Beach, Alva Andrews works on his student and Brenda's son, David Keoni Virden, using *iwi lomi*, lomilomi of the bones.

He "used me as a baker would a lump of dough. He worked me into this shape, then into that, then into no shape at all. My limbs became flat, or round, or neither at his will. My muscles were all relaxed and my joints seemed to have lost a sense of location. He put me back into the shape in which I came from Nature's mould, and I sank to sleep softly as an infant in its cradle. Ye who take to anodynes and inebriating potations to relieve a sense of pain, restlessness or fatigue try lomi-lomi." REV. WALTER COLTON, 1846

In her Honolulu lomilomi center,
Noelani manipulates the joints.
Watching over her is a picture of
her grandmother, Nana Veary,
author of the classic book,
Change We Must.

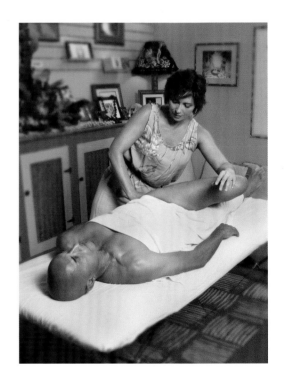

"*O*ur young attendant proceeds to knead and mould our limbs
with her small, well-shaped hands, tracing with dexterous fingers
the course of the tired muscles, and by her scientific manipulations
driving from them all latent aches and causing them to tingle
delightfully. Each joint is flexed and reflexed until one feels as
supine and limp as a rag. With a peculiar rolling motion, the
knuckles of the operatrix are moulded into the angles and curves
of the patient's body, and this is prolonged until all symptoms of
involuntary resistance have vanished, and he is rolled from side to
side and kneaded into a state of blissful lassitude that leaves nothing
to be desired in the way of perfect rest. . . . [continued]*

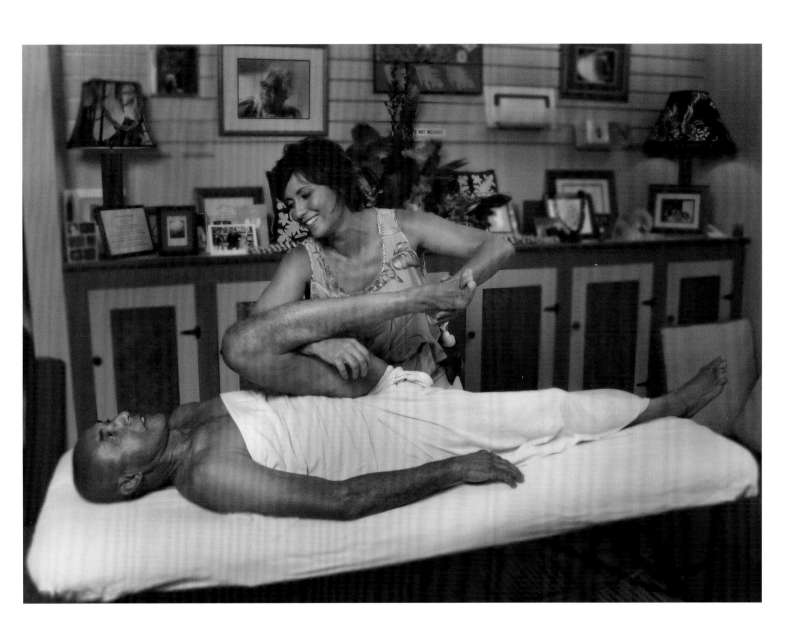

"*All the while the gentle palmists have been keeping up a ceaseless chatter with each other, that not only being totally unmeaning to us, but soft and harmonious with vocals, produces somewhat of the effect of merry waters rippling over a pebbly bed in some shady recess of a deep, cool wood. . . . There is a glorious feeling of rest stealing over us, and what with the lassitude consequent upon the lomi-lomi-ing, enhanced by the perfect quiet about us and the drowsy influence of the soft air stirring the rustling leaves of the thatch, we drop asleep.*"

ANONYMOUS VISITOR, 1892

Stomach Massage ⋮ 'Ōpū Huli

Kaliko Chang gives ʻōpū huli at Moku Ola Hawaiian Healing Center. Kaliko studied with Papa Kalua Kaiahua who said, "I don't massage — I reset."

Below: Papa Kalua always accompanied his treatments with jokes and laughter.

Papa Kalua Kaiahua came from the lua tradition of healing. He always began treatment with ʻōpū huli, *literally "turning stomach." The passages entering or exiting the stomach become twisted, so that nutrients and gastric gasses cannot properly pass through the digestive system. He manipulated the belly to clear the passages. "When it was my turn on the table, Papa Kalua put his hands on my ʻōpū, my stomach, and gently and firmly pressed and kneaded."*

MARTHA NOYES, 1996

Treading : 'A'e

Kamehanaokala Ruiz carefully treads on her mom, Patricia, while Maika'i Medeiros shows off his style. Both *keiki* study lomilomi at Moku Ola Hawaiian Healing Center.

I*n 1854, a visitor described another form of lomilomi — treading. "I have seen portly females extended upon the mats, face downwards, while juveniles, barefooted, were dancing upon their backs, and this they considered a luxury."* EDWARD T. PERKINS, 1854

"C*are was taken not to make any jerky movements lest there be an* 'anu'u, *that is, a dislocation of the spine."*

MARY KAWENA PUKUI, 1974

"Mrs. K would extend herself upon the mats, face downward;

after which a powerful man would elevate himself upon her back,

and pace up and down on her spine with a measured tread of a

wire dancer. This she esteemed a luxury, and it was a favorite

remedy on occasions of indigestion." EDWARD T. PERKINS, 1854

Hot Stones : **Pōhaku Wela**

Eri wraps hot stones in *kī* (ti) leaves.

L*omilomi is famous for using hot stones. Traditionally, hot stones wrapped in leaves are placed on the body. The heat of the stones releases the medicinal qualities of* noni, ti *or other leaves. Some modern practitioners use bare hot stones as hot packs, but caution must be used so as not to burn the skin.*

After wrapping the stones
in healing kī leaves, Eri places
them along the spine.

Lomi Sticks : **Lāʻau Lomi**

Koni crafts lomi sticks from guava wood found on the island of Hawai'i.

"The [Bishop] Museum possesses a number of specimens of 'lomilomi sticks,' curved implements of wood with long straight handles and lower ends crooked at an angle of about 45 degrees and flattened. The handle is held with both hands in front over the chest so that the implement curves over one shoulder and the flattened lower end may be pressed and drawn up and down on the upper muscles of the back; or the lower back muscles are massaged by holding the stick so that its crook curves around one or the other side of the body." HANDY, PUKUI, and LIVERMORE, 1934

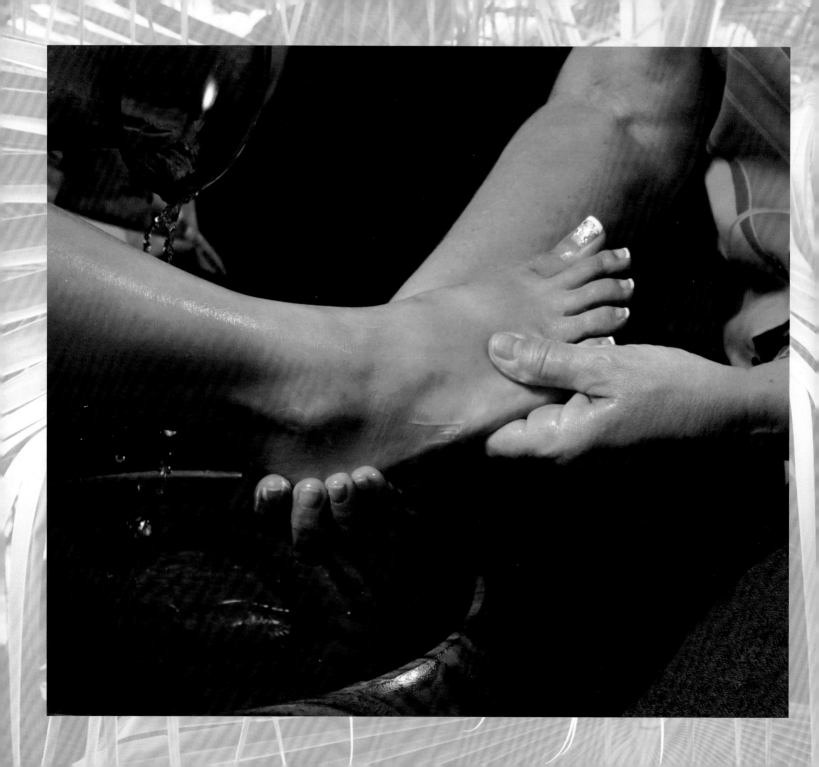

Foot Massage ⋮ **Lomi Wāwae**

"Our feet keep us firmly connected to the earth's energy center, the Pele energy, grounding and security. It is important to pay attention to our feet, as staying open and connected with this core energy allows us to manifest wondrous things, keeping us rooted and less affected by the world's fear and mental discord. When we treat the feet, the whole body gets treated."

BRENDA MOHALAPUA IGNACIO, 2004

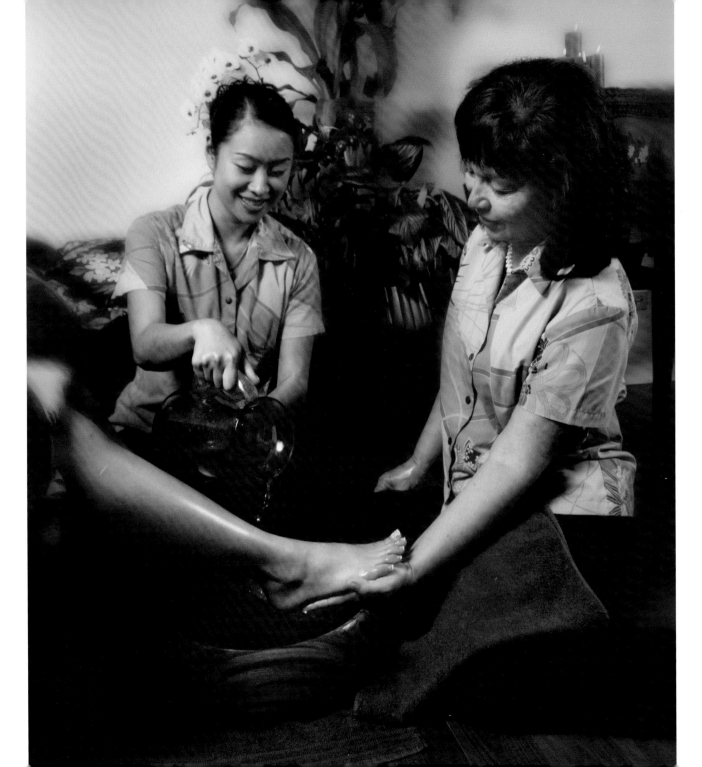

"Everything is in the feet—your head,
your heart, all your organs." PAPA K, 2007

Salt Rubs ⋮ Lomi Pa‘akai

Practitioners today sometimes rub clients with Hawaiian salt, or salt mixed with ʻalaea, *a red earth containing hematite. Traditionally, water with salt is used both internally and externally for spiritual cleansing. Salt is used as a poultice for fractures and sprains. ʻAlaea is taken internally as a tonic. Because salt traditionally was so valuable, historically, salt rubs may have been given only to aliʻi chiefs. The medicine of the salt and ʻalaea is absorbed through the skin, and the salt acts as a gentle exfoliant that leaves the skin softly glowing.*

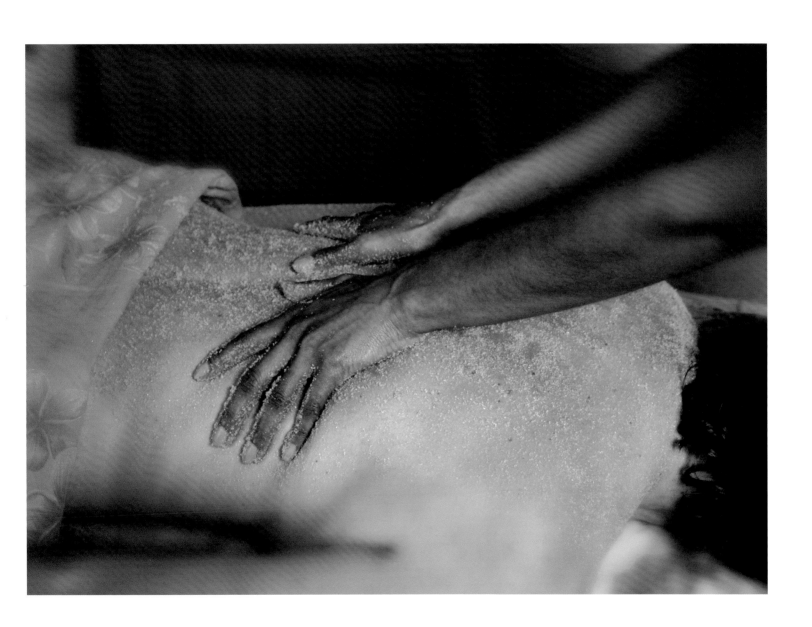

Malia is the granddaughter of
kumu lomilomi Angeline Locey,
below, who built this oversize
steam room for treatments.

"We *are honored to share our Hawaiian tradition of pa'akai at*
Angeline's. Pa'akai is one of three sacred elements of old Hawaiian
culture, along with Kalo and Ti leaf. All three have spiritually
protective and healing properties. Pa'akai is crystalline in nature,
and crystal has spiritual (metaphysical) as well as physical
qualities. It has many wonderful spiritual and medicinal uses."

MICHAEL LOCEY, 2006

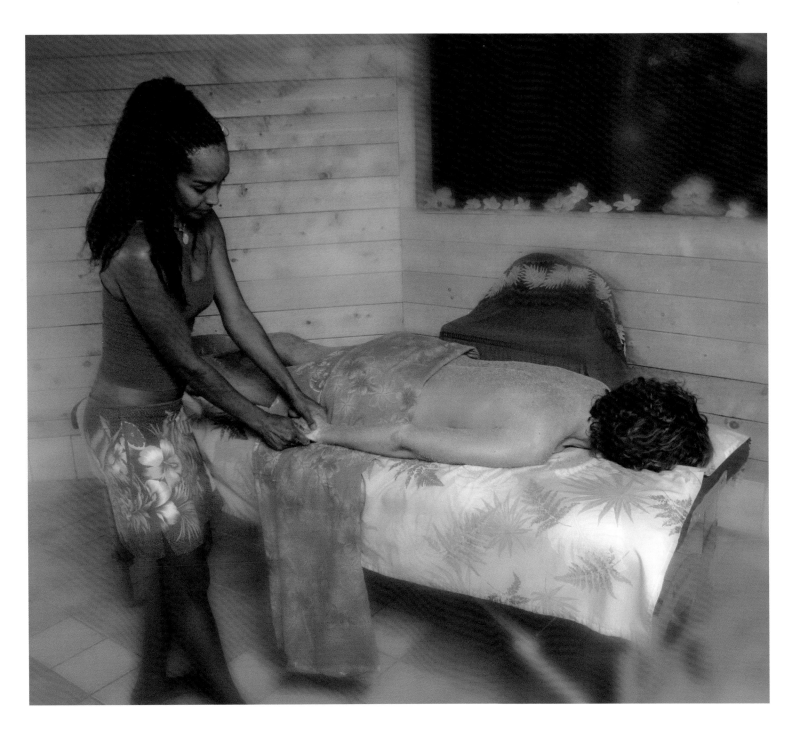

Water Treatments : **Wai Ola**

The first Hawaiians discovered natural steam baths at the volcanoes on the island of Hawai'i. They created steam by heating water in a bowl or gourd and placing it with the patient under a *kapa* (tapa) blanket.

"The lomi-lomi is a very ancient and famous practice among the Hawaiians and consists of a complicated kneading, rubbing, and pinching of the skin and muscles of the body, and is considered quite a luxury. The steam bath followed by the lomi-lomi is a very good substitute for the Turkish bath so popular in Europe and America." CHARLES DAVIDSON, M.D., 1899

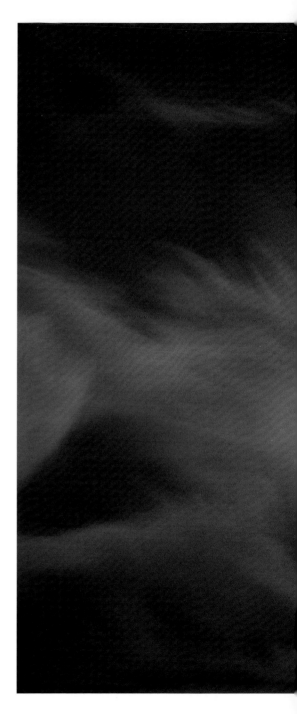

Dane Kaohelani Silva treats his
daughter, Shelle, in the hot pond
on the island of Hawaiʻi.

The healers of old recommended warm baths to cure a dull
headache, and for "the sickness that comes at house building time."
"In special places along the eastern coast of Hawaiʻi, pools of
geothermally heated water are used daily for their healing
powers by bathers. The warm, buoyant water soothes muscles
and arthritic joints while reducing the full effects of gravity."

DANE KAOHELANI SILVA, 2000

Hawaiians also use cool fresh water as a remedy. "A gentle
waterfall relaxes stiffness and relieves pain. Cold water that seeps
through the lava tubes from the mountains to pour into ponds
at the shore is used to stimulate deep circulation. Immersion in
fresh water is often the final part of a course of treatment."

DANE KAOHELANI SILVA, 2000

Family Massage : ʻOhana Lomilomi

Previous: Michael Locey and his daughter, Malia, in the garden at Angeline's.

Opposite and below: Aunty Mary Fragas, renowned for her work with pregnant women, shows a husband how to give lomilomi to his wife and child. The baby's heartbeat can be felt through the mother's *piko* (navel).

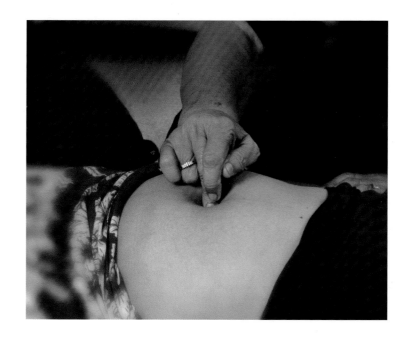

Traditionally, everyone in the family practiced lomilomi. They gave each other massage to relieve sore muscles, headaches, and indigestion, as well as for pure enjoyment. From before the time they were born, children received lomilomi from their parents and grandparents. They were massaged throughout childhood.

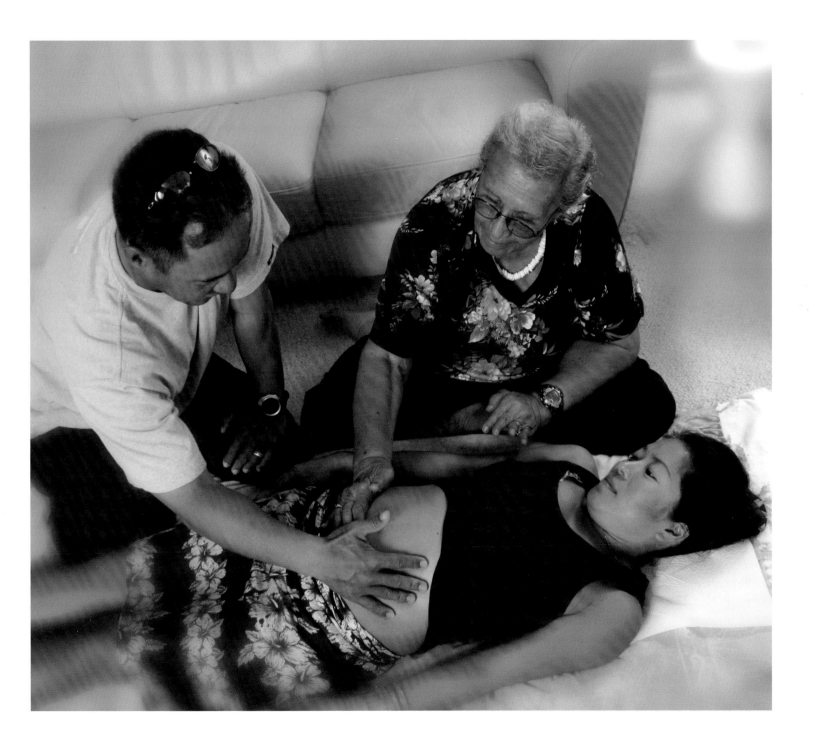

Kaliko teaches Maika'i
and Kamehanaokala
how to lomi the legs.

*Parents also taught their children to use lomilomi as basic first
aid. After a long trip walking for weeks around the Big Island, a
Hawaiian "seated himself on a mat on the floor, while his brothers
and sisters gathered around him; some unloosed his sandals,
and rubbed his limbs and feet."* REV. WILLIAM ELLIS, 1822

LiAnn needs only a chair to work
on Mary, a surfer, a few blocks
from Waikīkī Beach.

While learning to surf from Duke Kahanamoku in about 1913,

an American woman crashed into an outrigger canoe and fell

on the reef. "Duke reached the spot, clutched me by the back and

spreading me out upon a surfboard gave me the famous Hawaiian

lomi-lomi . . . and in a few minutes I was able to join the party

as good as new." LEOLA M. CRAWFORD, 1913

Michael and Malia give each other foot lomi, while Donald Kaiahua massages Liz's neck and shoulders.

"The lomi-lomi is used not only by the natives, but among almost all the foreign residents; and not merely to procure relief from weariness consequent on overexertion, but to cure headache, to relieve the aching of neuralgic or rheumatic pains, and, by the luxurious, as one of the pleasures of life."

CHARLES NORDHOFF, 1874

Learning Lomilomi ⋮ **A'o**

Previous: Donald teaches his
grandson, Hekili.

Opposite: "Pure Hawaiian Boy,
1906." Does this boy have
the soul of a kahuna?

*H*ow do practitioners learn the art of lomilomi? In old Hawai'i,
the most skilled healers began intense training at an early age. "If
the parents or particularly the grandparents noticed that a child's
behavior seemed to be unusually kind and thoughtful towards his
[or her] parents and towards his brothers and sisters, if he seemed
to be particularly concerned about his playmates when they were
injured or in distress, one of the grandparents or parents might say,
'I think this boy has the soul of a kahuna lapaau.' If, after further
observation, they decided that this was correct, they would send
the boy to the kahuna lapaau of the community." JOHN DESHA, 1951

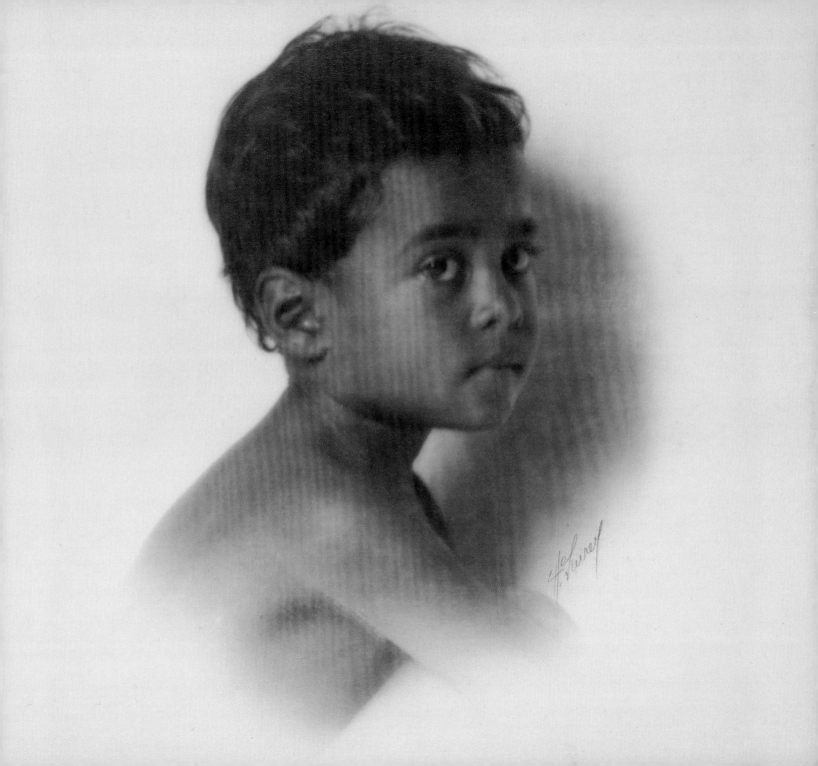

At the ruins of Keaīwa heiau,
a healing temple on Oʻahu,
Brenda prays. Medicinal trees
and herbs surround the temple.

The *kāhuna received their training at a school in a healing temple. "In all of Polynesia, only in Hawaiʻi were there such heiau hoʻola (healing temple) for . . . training of* haumana *(students) with a rigorous 20-year or so curriculum. . . ."*

KEKUNI BLAISDELL, M.D., 1993

Papa Auwae's grandson,
Kehaulani Keopuhiwa, with his
wife, Jeanella, continue Papa's
traditions in the village of Volcano
on the island of Hawai'i.

Today, *many train with their family members. "I started to learn
how to be a healer at the age of 7 from my great-grandmother.
I have learned for 73 years, and I worked with my great-
grandmother until she died at 106. We practiced at home
in Kawaihae and at Lapakahi."* PAPA HENRY AUWAE, 1991

Auntie Margaret Machado "grew up with lomilomi. Her grand-father, John Aha'ula Keali'i Au, passed the art on to her. When she was about 10, he leaned over and breathed on her four times — on each cheek, her forehead, and the top of her head — and then chanted over her in Hawaiian." AUNTIE NERITA MACHADO, 2006

Forgiveness : **Ho'oponopono**

Previous: Kumu hula Keala Ching, a hoʻoponopono practitioner, offers an *oli* (sacred chant) in the rainforest on the slopes of Mauna Loa.

Donald and Yvonne Kaiahua, *opposite*, and Jeanella and Kehaulani Keopuhiwa, *below,* know that sometimes all you need for lōkahi is a smile and a hug.

Before beginning a lomilomi session, the kahuna might also conduct a hoʻoponopono session. Hoʻoponopono (pronounced ho-o-po-no-po-no) means "setting to right," "forgiveness," "reconciliation," or "family counseling." "Hoʻoponopono *is a traditional system for restoring* lōkahi, *or harmony, within the client and their* ʻohana *(extended family). Many lomilomi practitioners are trained in the basic aspects of this art.*" DANE KAOHELANI SILVA, 2000

Early Hawaiians knew what modern medicine has now proved
— holding grudges makes you sick. Only forgiveness and reconciliation could heal such sickness. "Maʻi ma loko *was sickness from* loko,
'within.' *But not within the body. Within the family. Quarrels and
holding grudges and* hihia *[ill feeling from unforgiven hostilities]
and* hukihuki *[power struggle] and general unpleasantness in the
family. All this caused sickness."* MARY KAWENA PUKUI, 1972

In the 19th century, there was "a woman who had been ill for a long time. She was terribly bloated, her heart was affected.... Just the weight of the sheet was torture to her. The kahuna told ... the mother that the woman had committed ten secret sins; for her to ask the woman about it and if she confessed and was repentant she could be cured. If not, then nothing could be done for her. The mother talked to her daughter and she said the kahuna was right; she confessed and repented.... In the morning, ... the woman was walking on the lanai and was perfectly normal and well."

MR. McGUIRE, 1933

Kaipo Kaneakua says, "Your trust, your honesty, your truth — that is what heals you."

Guilt, grudges, jealousies, bitterness, anger, fear — these secrets increase blood pressure, anxiety, and stress. Forgiveness and reconciliation have been proven to reduce blood pressure, anxiety, and stress. "Amidst Hawaiian tears and laughter forgiveness was asked and given. The old man [kahuna] . . . spoke words of cleansing, and warned that the trouble should not be remembered."

MAX FREEDOM LONG, 1954

Allen Alapaʻi and his wife, Antoinette,
with friends. Uncle Allen, of Hanalei,
loves to blow bubbles as a reminder
of the importance of hā, the sacred
breath of life.

"My grandmother said, 'Forgiveness is the key that opens the heart.' The thing that gets in the way of the heart is the mind. Turn off the mind. The mind is not us, it is other people's voices. Once we forgive the voices, the mind turns off. When the mind goes off, the heart opens. Life is a feeling, not a thinking." ALLEN ALAPAʻI, 2005

Sacred Touch : **Lomilomi Kāpu**

Today, some lomilomi practitioners use ho'oponopono and prayer to achieve a deep healing experience. Others bring a sense of reverence to a "simple" massage, allowing you to feel forgiveness through their loving touch. Whatever you seek, there is a lomilomi experience for your unique needs.

As the lomilomi comes to an end,
the receiver slowly opens her eyes
and sees the world in a sacred light.

"I could not have fallen into gentler hands. There was a strength in her finger tips, and healing in her presence, and she imparted both to me." HELEN MATHER, 1891

Glossary of Hawaiian Words

'āina – land

akua, Akua – gods, God

ali'i – chief, the chiefly class, nobles, royalty

aloha – love, compassion, caring

'aumakua – family gods

hā – breath, breathe, exhale, life

hālau – long house, school (as in hula hālau)

hale – house

haumana – student, disciple

heiau – temple

ho'oponopono – forgiveness and reconciliation process

iwi – bone, bones

kahu – pastor, minister, reverend, guardian

kahuna – priest, expert, master

kāhuna – plural of kahuna

kalo – taro

kanaka – person

kānaka – plural of kanaka

kānaka maoli – Native Hawaiians

kāne – man, male

kapa – tapa (cloth made from bark)

keiki – child, children

kōkua – help, assistance

kumu – teacher

kupuna – elder, ancestor, grandparent

kūpuna – plural of kupuna

lā'au lapa'au – herbal medicine

lānai – verandah, balcony

lōkahi – harmony, unity

lua – Hawaiian martial art

mahalo – thank you

mana – supernatural, divine or spiritual power, energy

maoli – native, indigenous

'ohana – family, extended family

'ōlohe – skilled master

pā – lua school

poi – the Hawaiian staff of life, made from pounded, cooked taro, thinned with water

pule – prayer

wailele – waterfall

Directory of Lomilomi Practitioners

There are wonderful practitioners in Hawai'i and around the world, and we have yet to meet them all. These are just a few we know and love. Choosing to receive a treatment from or studying with a lomilomi teacher is a matter of your *kuleana,* your individual responsibility; the authors and publisher do not warrant their performance and disclaim any and all liability. Information listed is believed to be correct as of February 2007. In some places we list kumu who have retired or passed on, and then list the members of their 'ohana who carry on their tradition.

Hawaiian Lomilomi Association

P.O. Box 2356
Kealakekua, HI 96750-2356
www.hawaiilomilomi.com

HLA has an annual conference in Hawai'i. Its web site lists kumu and practitioners from around the world who have studied with certified teachers.

Allen Elia Keala Alapa'i
Antoinette Kahili Alapa'i

P.O. Box 841
Hanalei, Kaua'i, HI 96714
808-826-6604
halehooponopono@yahoo.com
www.AllenAlapai.com

Allen learned from his grandmother to nurture the *keiki kāne, keiki wahine* — the baby boy, baby girl — in ourselves and everyone, and he is a living example. He sings his own songs, plays 'ukulele, and practices ho'oponopono lomilomi to release all the tension and knots that negative energies cause, to bring the body, mind, heart and spirit into balance. Featured in the film, "Pule Wailele," Allen teaches on Kaua'i, in Western Europe and on the U.S. mainland.

Alva James Andrews
Ka Pā Ola

Waimānalo, HI 96795
808-259-5000
808-429-9471

Alva is a Native Hawaiian, a father, grandfather and Vietnam War veteran. His love and passion is his gift of spiritual and physical healing which he uses and teaches. He is a practitioner of lua, the Hawaiian martial art that has as its foundation the understanding of how bones are broken and reset. He learned body alignment from Papa Kalua Kaiahua, and lua from 'Ōlohe Mitchell Eli, D.C. Alva also is a noted graphic artist.

Noelani Bennett, L.M.T.
Hands Toward Heaven
1113 Kapahulu Ave.
Honolulu, HI 96816
808-737-7770
lominoe@gmail.com
www.handstowardheaven.net

Raised on Oʻahu, Noelani was mentored by her pure Hawaiian grandmother, Nana Veary, who was a well-loved teacher, author and spiritual counselor. Noelani began her formal instruction with Margaret Machado in 1979. A Licensed Massage Therapist, for many years she taught at the Honolulu School of Massage and Kapiʻolani Community College. Today she teaches at her lomilomi center on Oʻahu, and in Japan and Europe.

Kaliko Chang, L.M.T.
Moku Ola Hawaiian Healing Center
7192 Kalanianaʻole Hwy, #D-201
Honolulu, HI 96825
808-394-6658
kc99@onebox.com

Born and raised on Oʻahu, Kaliko became interested in lomilomi as a child while observing "Uncle Bob" lomi his family. He met Uncle Kalua Kaiahua in 1993 and then studied with him and later with Auntie Margaret Machado. He is grateful to have spent time and learned with other kūpuna and practitioners throughout Hawaiʻi and the Pacific. He believes in helping to perpetuate Hawaiian healing to promote the overall health and welfare of all people.

M. Keala Ching
Executive Director
Kumu Nā Wai Iwi Ola Foundation
P.O. Box 3647
Kailua-Kona, HI 96745
(808) 355-8889
www.nawaiiwiola.org
mkeala@turquoise.net

Keala, a dancer with The Men of Waimapuna under the direction of Darryl Ihiihilauakea Lupenui, competed in 1984 in the King Kamehameha Hula & Chant competition as well as the Merrie Monarch Hula Festival in 1986. In 1999, Keala became a practitioner of hoʻoponopono with Kupuna Malia Craver, a cultural specialist at the Queen Liliʻuokalani Children's Center. He is a practitioner of hula, and Hawaiian culture and traditions with Kumu Hula Kawaikapuokalani Hewett, of Kūhai Hālau Kawaikapuokalani Pā ʻŌlapa Kahiko.

Mary Fragas
2506 Kīlauea Ave.
Hilo, HI 96720
808-959-8043

In 1929, at age six, Aunty Mary was paralyzed by polio. After years of massage by parents and Hawaiian healers and her innate determination, she was able to walk with support. This courage afforded her a full life of career, marriage and raising five children. Her sharp mind and prayers led her to mastery of body knowledge and function. Her mission is to restore health to those who come to her. Her delightful personality and joy light up any setting, as seen in the film "Hawaiian Healing."

Kawaikapuokalani Hewett
kahalelehua@hotmail.com
www.kahalelehua.com
www.kahuna888.com
www.hulapele.com

Kawaikapuokalani is renowned internationally as a kumu hula and composer, and has been a judge for many hula competitions, including the Merrie Monarch Festival. Kawaikapu is also renowned in the old traditions of Hawaiian healing arts, and offers prayer, spiritual counseling, lomilomi and lāʻau lapaʻau. In healing traditions, he was the sole protégé of Kahuna Emma deFries, recognized as a true kahuna and descendant of Hewahewa. Makana (the author of this book) considers herself blessed to be part of the ʻohana of Kawaikapu, who is cousin to her husband Mark.

Haunani Hopkins, L.M.T.
Mana Hopkins
P.O. Box 2356
Kealakekua, HI 96750-2356
808-324-7202
mapunawaiola@msn.com
www.mapunawaiola.com

Haunani, descended from the Kaʻuhane family of Kaʻu, on the island of Hawaiʻi, is a Licensed Massage Therapist who studied with Auntie Margaret Machado, Makaʻala Yates, D.C., and Dane Kaohelani Silva. But she calls her greatest teacher Ke Akua. She says, "Ke Akua guides our hands through our hearts." Haunani's interview is one of the highlights of the film "Hawaiian Healing." Her daughter, Mana, continues in the family tradition. Haunani teaches lomilomi on the island of Hawaiʻi.

Brenda Mohalapua Ignacio, L.M.T.
Lomilomi Hana Lima
315 Uluniu Street, Suite 202
Kailua, HI 96734
808-263-0303

bignacio808@aol.com
www.LomilomiHanaLima.com
www.lomilomialoha.com

A native of Hāmākua on the island of Hawaiʻi, Brenda was taught from birth the connection of the spirit of love in all things. Her training began with hula, and she continues to dance professionally. She is an L.M.T. and is passionate about teaching. Her most influential teachers were Hannah "Nana" Veary, Auntie Margaret Machado and Makaʻala Yates. Before establishing Lomilomi Hana Lima with her family, she co-founded Hawaiʻi Healing Arts College, starting the lomilomi program there. She inspired the film "Hawaiian Healing" and has been the guiding light of this book.

Donald Kaiahua
Yvonne Momi Kaiahua,
Geraldlyn Kaiahua,
Alexandra Couldwell,
Hekili Hiraga-Kaiahua
446 Puako Way
Kailua, HI 96734
808-262-9509

Donald was born on Molokaʻi and grew up in Kalihi on Oʻahu with his family, including brothers Kalua and Arthur

who are also known for lomilomi. He started apprenticeship at age six with his father practicing hoʻoponopono and lāʻau lapaʻau. Annie Bunker Usesugi taught him *lima hāhā* (feeling with the hands). This style lets your fingers tell you a person's condition. Its touch is a soft and gentle pressure only from the hands and fingers. His three daughters and grandson continue his legacy.

Parker Kaipo Kaneakua
P.O. Box 2427
Honolulu, HI 96804
808-226-5556
Kaneakua55@yahoo.co.jp

Kaipo learned about healing from 16 family kūpuna, from Molokaʻi, Hawaiʻi, and Oʻahu, from his father, Joseph K. Kaneakua, Sr., of Kauaʻi, and his Molokaʻi grandmother, Elizabeth Koahou. Each kupuna specialized in different types of healing, methods of treatment. Although he grew up and now lives on Oʻahu, most of his life he practiced on Maui. He says, "I do not call what I do lomilomi, because I prefer to work with sick people." He practices lāʻau lapaʻau, *lomi kūpele* (soft kneading), hoʻoponopono and *hoʻomaʻemaʻe* (cleansing).

Abraham Kawai'i 'ohana
Ho'okahi Ho'oulu, Sonia Kamali'i,
Faye Kawa'ilani Hope Kumu
Na Pua 'Olohe
P.O. Box 1059
Kapa'a, Kaua'i, HI 96795
808-822-0283
napuaolohe@gmail.com
www.napuaolohe.com

Na Pua 'Olohe was founded by Abraham
Kawai'i for the promotion and teaching
of Kahuna Sciences as developed for
Western culture. Ho'okahi, his wife,
is a recognized and accomplished
student of the masters: Hawaiian
Kahuna Abraham Kawai'i ('ike), Kahuna
Aui'ia Maka'i'ole (uliama) and Ho'oulu
Lahui Manawehi (kaukahi). Sonia and
Faye are Kahu's daughters and continue
the traditions they learned growing
up with his teachings.

Kehau & Jeanella Keopuhiwa, L.M.T.
Na Lima Aukahi
P.O. Box 463
Volcano, HI 96785
808-967-7439
goodmedicine@fernforest.net
www.fernforest.net

A Licensed Massage Therapist, Jeanella
is a practitioner of lomilomi massage
and lā'au lapa'au. Her lomilomi training
includes studying loving touch with
Aunty Margaret. Papa Henry Auwae,
her husband Kehau's grandfather, chose
Jeanella as 'ohana and haumana to carry
on his work after his passing, thereby
honoring seven generations of Hawaiian
healers in this 'ohana. Jeanella and
Kehau continue the legacy of their
kūpuna on the island of Hawai'i.

Sylvester "Papa K" Kepilino
1856 Kino'ole St.
Hilo, HI 96720
808-989-3963
www.healinginparadise.org

Kiliwelu Kamaka Iki Ali'i Pa'akaula Kamoa
Kamoa, better known as Papa K, was born
in 1929 in Ho'okena. He began his training in lomilomi at the age of six from his
grandfather, John Pa'akaula. He learned
the healing of broken bones through
breathing from his father, Sylvester. In
the 1970s he began teaching lomilomi
and the Hawaiian language on O'ahu.
He teaches workshops in Canada,
Europe and on the U.S. mainland, and
is featured in the film "Pule Wailele."

Koni / Koni Lomi
P.O. Box 2267
Pāhoa, HI 96778
808-938-7467

Koni crafts lomi sticks from guava wood
and uses them for muscle stretching and
trigger point therapy. He can be found
on the island of Hawai'i at lomi events
and at the Pāhoa Farmer's Market.

Angeline Kaihalanaopuna Hopkins
Locey (Retired)
Michael Locey, Malia Locey
Angeline's
4410 Malama 'Āina Pl., Lot 19
Anahola, Kaua'i, HI 96703
808-652-3411
mjlocey@hawaii.rr.com
www.AuntyAngelines.com

Born in 1929, Aunty Angeline is of both
Hawaiian and English ancestry. As a
young woman she danced hula and then
married, raised children and became a
nurse. In the 1970s she learned lomilomi
from Auntie Margaret. In about 1985
she moved to Kaua'i and built her spa
on homestead land that at one time
was part of the Kahua Heiau complex.
Her son Michael and his daughter Malia
continue giving lomilomi, and Malia also
continues the family tradition in hula.

The Lomi Shop Va'a
Mana Hawaii Spirit of Hawaii Nei
Waikiki Beachwalk, 2nd floor
808-923-2220
www.manahawaiinei.com
Windward Mall, 2nd floor
808-234-5664
www.lomi.com

The Lomi Shop Va'a (canoe) offers a "Voyage through Health and Wellness." Seated Lomi and Foot Lomi massage treatments begin your journey. Return for complete one-hour Lomi treatments and enhance your experience with Native Oils, Lā'au Lapa'au and Lomi music for the soul. With two locations, one in Waikīkī and the other in Kāne'ohe, visitors and residents to the island of O'ahu enjoy the opportunity to learn more about the culture and spirit of Hawai'i through lomilomi.

Margaret Machado (Retired)
Nerita Onaona Machado, L.M.T.
Hawaiian Massage Salon
P.O. Box 221
Captain Cook, HI 96704
808-323-2416
auntie_margaret@hawaiiantel.net
www.lomilomimassage.com

Nerita, a Native Hawaiian, was born to Margaret and Daniel Machado on O'ahu. The family moved to Napo'opo'o in 1949 and Nerita feels blessed to have grown up in a fishing village living the old ways. Nerita graduated from college in Washington state with a B.S. in nursing, and worked as a nurse for many years on the mainland before coming home in 1991 to assist her mother. She earned her L.M.T. in 1997 and began teaching in 2000.

Tamara Conlan Mondragon, L.M.T.
Hawaiian Healing Arts
Hawai'i: 808-347-1454
California: 805-390-7731
www.lomilomi.com
tamara@lomilomi.com

Tamara's lomilomi apprenticeship with Auntie Margaret began in 1973, when there was no formal school. She feels honored to have worked one on one with Auntie, which led to her receiving her license from the State of Hawai'i in September 1974. Tamara continues sharing lomilomi in many ways, including teaching, writing a cover story for *Massage Magazine,* and creating instructional videos, workbooks and other aids designed to enhance learning this ancient healing art.

Jeana Iwalani Naluai, L.M.T.
Kamaile Puaoi, L.M.T.
Ho'omana Restorative Therapies
1550 Pi'iholo Rd.
Makawao, Maui, HI 96768
808-283-4767
jeana@lomimassage.com
www.lomimassage.com

Jeana is a Native Hawaiian committed to perpetuating her culture through the healing arts. Jeana holds these islands very close to her heart, dancing hula, playing Hawaiian music, and "living aloha." She is a Physical Therapist and has studied Hawaiian healing under many kūpuna and kumu throughout the Islands. Her lifelong dream has been realized by opening a retreat center on Maui where she holds workshops in lomilomi and practices Hawaiian Healing. Kamaile is her dear friend and teaching assistant.

Henry Kaleiwohi "Uncle Butch" Richards

Born on O'ahu, Uncle Butch grew up on Maui and learned healing from the age of five from his great-grandparents, Charles Moses Kahinuonalani Kamakawiwaole and Daisy Ka'aiawaawa Kaleiwohi of

Honoka'a on the island of Hawai'i. He is featured in the film, "Pule Wailele." He holds a master's degree in Pacific Island Studies, and taught Hawaiian culture as a kupuna in various intermediate and high schools on O'ahu for 35 years. He is an active member of the Historic Preservation Council of the Office of Hawaiian Affairs.

Wes Waianiani Sen, L.M.T.
Lehua McCandless
Judson Kealohakeikihipa McCandless

1529 Ala Amoamo Street
Honolulu, HI 96819
808-854-9283
Fax: 310-828-2449
wailanamaliehawaii@yahoo.com
www.lomihawaii.com

Wes is from Moanalua, O'ahu, the ancestral home of his wife Lehua McCandless. Wes is an L.M.T. and colon hydrotherapist who studied with Auntie Margaret, the late Uncle Kalua Kaiahua, and Cook Island Aitutaki back-walking master Uncle Freddie Tiramakea. He and Lehua teach lomilomi on the mainland, in Hawai'i and in Japan. They carry on the work of Auntie Margaret's Hawaiian Sea Water Colon Cleanse at their Makapala retreat center in Kohala. Judson is their nephew and student.

Dane Kaohelani Silva, L.M.T.
Hawaiian Healing Center

HCR2 Box 6281
Kea'au, HI 96749
808-965-8917
kumulomi@haleola.com
www.haleola.com

Dane learned Hawaiian healing from his grandmother, Lily Kakani Nobriga, of Hāna, Maui, Uncle Harry Mitchell and Papa Henry Auwae. He earned his doctoral degree in chiropractic, is certified in acupuncture, is a Licensed Massage Therapist, and is the founder of the Hawaiian Healing Center. Also one of the founders of the Hawaiian Lomilomi Association, he is an instructor for vocational, college and graduate programs in Hawai'i, North America, Europe, New Zealand and Japan. He is featured in the film, "Hawaiian Healing."

Ramsay Taum

531 Hahaione Street 19A
Honolulu, HI 96825
808-394-5557
halaulua@hawaii.rr.com

Ramsay Taum is a practitioner of Kaihewalu lua, lomi hāhā (feeling with the hands), and ho'oponopono. Before he could learn to "break," he needed to

learn to "fix." His teachers and mentors included renowned kāhuna lapa'au, historians, philosophers, statesmen and respected elders including Auntie Morrnah Nalamaku Simeona, Auntie Pilahi Paki, Uncle Tommy Solomon, Uncle John Pe'a, Tutu Kale (Charles) Kenn, John Dominis Holt III, Donald Kilolani Mitchell, Uncle Al Grace, Papa Richard Lyman, and 'Ōlohe Solomon Kaihewalu. Makana is blessed to be a member of his 'ohana.

LiAnn Uyeda, L.M.T.
Aloha Lomilomi

449 Kapahulu Ave., #205
Honolulu, HI 96815
808-738-5244
alohalomilomi@hotmail.com
www.alohalomilomi.com

LiAnn grew up on O'ahu where she practiced her first love, hula. Currently she dances with Blaine Kamalani Kia's Hālau, Ka Waikahe Lani Malie. She graduated from massage school and established her Hawaiian Healing Hale in 1993. She has been inspired and educated by Maka'ala Yates, D.C., Papa K Kepilino, Aunty Mary Fragas and Aunty Mahealani Kuamo'o-Henry. She teaches "Aloha Lōkahi Lomilomi" on O'ahu and Maui, and in Japan and Australia.

Eri Mahealani Sakai Virden, L.M.T.
Lomilomi Hana Lima
315 Uluniu Street, Suite 202
Kailua, HI 96734
808-263-0303
eri_isle@hotmail.com
www.LomilomiHanaLima.com

Born in Nagoya, Japan, as a child Eri visited Hawai'i with her family. She studies hula with Hawaiian Kumu Hula Kapua Dalire and competed in the Merrie Monarch Festival in 2000 and 2007. After learning physiology and aromatherapy, she studied lomilomi with Dane Silva and operated a lomilomi practice in Japan. At a Hawaiian Lomi-lomi Association Conference, Eri met David Keoni Virden, Brenda Ignacio's son, and they married in 2005. The three established their healing center, Lomilomi Hana Lima, in 2006.

Aoi Wright, L.M.T.
Moku Ola Hawaiian Healing Center
7192 Kalaniana'ole Hwy., #D-201
Honolulu, HI 96825
808-394-6658
aoi@mokuolahawaii.com
www.mokuolahawaii.com

Together with Pi'ilani Wright, Aoi owns Moku Ola Hawaiian Healing Center at Koko Marina in East O'ahu. Aoi first learned Hawaiian healing from her *tūtū*

man (grandfather), Joe Keo Wright. She practiced nursing for 10 years, then attended massage school and became a Licensed Massage Therapist. She studied the tradition of Auntie Margaret with Sheila O'Malley and the tradition of Papa Kalua Kaiahua with Kaliko Chang. She dances hula with Nā Pualei O Likolehua, led by Kumu Hula Leina'ala Kalama Heine, and competed in the Merrie Monarch in 2006.

Maka'ala Yates, D.C.
Hawaiian Healing Institute
P.O. Box 726
Ashland, OR 97520
541-488-5879 or 541-301-2896
hhi@hawaiianlomi.org
www.hawaiianlomi.org

Maka'ala is a Kanaka Maoli (Native Hawaiian) who specializes in the full spectrum of Hawaiian medicine. He has been practicing and teaching for over 25 years, trained by Hawaiian healing experts in his native place, the island of Hawai'i. In July 2006, he was honored with the Kaonohi Award, presented by Papa Ola Lōkahi, for his dedicated service and outstanding work in Hawaiian medi-cine. Through his Kōkua (Assistance) Program, he and his students provide lomilomi free in Hawaiian communities.

All the historic quotes in this book were originally published in the comprehensive study of lomilomi, *Nā Moʻolelo Lomilomi: The Traditions of Hawaiian Massage and Healing* (Bishop Museum Press, 2005), edited by R. Makana Risser Chai.

Alapaʻi, Allen. Presentation at Hawaiian Lomilomi Association Conference, September 18, 2005.

Auwae, Henry, quoted in *Wai Ola o OHA*, Nov. 1991, p. 15.

Blaisdell, Kekuni, M.D. "Historical and Philosophical Aspects of Lapaʻau — Traditional Kānaka Maoli Healing Practices." *He Ala Ā He Alo.* Hawaiʻi: American Friends Service Committee, 1993, p. 44–45.

Brigham, William T. "Laau Lomilomi Kua." *Ancient Hawaiian House.* Memoirs of Bernice Pauahi Bishop Museum, vol. 2, no. 3, 1908, p. 313–314.

Colton, Rev. Walter, U.S.N. *Deck and Port.* New York: Evans & Co., 1850, p. 347.

Crawford, Leola M. *An American Girl: Seven Weeks in Hawaii.* San Francisco: John Newbegin, 1917.

Davidson, Charles. "Hawaiian Medicine: Second Installment." *The Queen's Hospital Bulletin* (September 1927): 4(4).

Desha, John, quoted in Larsen, Nils P. "Rededication of the Healing Heiau Keaiwa." Reprinted from the *60th Annual Report of the Hawaiian Historical Society.* Honolulu, 1951. p. 7–16.

Ellis, Rev. William. *Journal of William Ellis, Narrative of a Tour of Hawaii, or Owhyhee; with Remarks on the History, Traditions Manners, Customs, and Language of the Inhabitants of the Sandwich Islands.* Rutland, VT: Charles E. Tuttle Company, 1979.

Emerson, Joseph S. "Selections from a Kahuna's Book of Prayers." In *Hawaiian Historical Society 26th Annual Report.* Honolulu: Paradise of the Pacific Press, 1918, p. 17–39.

Handy, E. S. Craighill, Mary Kawena Pukui, and Katherine Livermore. *Outline of Hawaiian Physical Therapeutics.* Bernice P. Bishop Museum Bulletin 126. Honolulu: Bishop Museum Press, 1934.

Ignacio, Brenda Mohalapua. Presentation at Hawaiian Lomilomi Association Conference, September 18, 2004.

Jarves, James Jackson. *History of the Hawaiian or Sandwich Islands.* Boston: Tappan and Dennet, 1843, p. 87–88.

Jensen, Lucia Tarallo, and Natalie Mahina Jensen. *Daughters of Haumea: Nā Kaikamahine 'o Haumea, Women of Ancient Hawai'i.* San Francisco, CA: Pueo Press, 2005.

Kahalewai, Nancy S., L.M.T. *Hawaiian Lomilomi: Big Island Massage.* Mountain View, HI: Island Massage Publishing, 2000.

Kawai'i, Abraham. *Na Pua 'Olohe: The Flowers of Wisdom.* Kapa'a, HI: Na Pua 'Olohe, 2003.

Kelly, Marilyn. "The Ins and Outs of Local Massage." *Hawaii Observer,* October 6, 1977, p. 22.

Lewis, Jimmy, quoted in Bowman, Sally-Jo. "Lomilomi's Loving Touch." *Aloha,* November/December 1996, p. 33.

Lili'uokalani. *Hawaii's Story by Hawaii's Queen, 1898.* Honolulu: Tuttle Co., 1964.

Locey, Michael. Personal correspondence, January 6, 2007.

Long, Max Freedom. *The Secret Science Behind Miracles.* Santa Monica: De Vorss, 1954.

Machado, Margaret, quoted in Harden, M.J. *Voices of Wisdom: Hawaiian Elders Speak.* Kula, HI: Aka Press, 1999.

Machado, Nerita. Personal interview. 2006.

Mather, Helen. *One Summer in Hawaii.* New York: Cassell, 1891.

McGuire, Mr. "Manuscript," 1933, Bernice Pauahi Bishop Museum Archives MS SC Handy, Box 7.6.

Mondragon, Tamara. "Lomilomi: Ancient Hawaiian Healing Art." *Massage Magazine,* July/August 2000, p. 78.

Nordhoff, Charles. *Northern California, Oregon and the Sandwich Isles.* New York: Harper, 1874.

Noyes, Martha. "A Choice of Cure." *Aloha.* March/April 1996, p. 24.

Olmsted, Emma Akana. Interview, June 13, 1933, Bernice Pauahi Bishop Museum Archives MS SC Handy, Box 7.7, p. 53.

Olmsted, Emma Akana. Interview, July 6, 1930, Bernice Pauahi Bishop Museum Archives HEN, Vol. 1, p. 106.

Olmsted, Emma Akana. Interview, July 2, 1933, Bernice Pauahi Bishop Museum Archives MS SC Handy, Box 7.7, p. 52.

Perkins, Edward T. *Na Motu: Reef-Rovings in the South Seas.* New York: Garrett, 1854.

Pukui, Mary Kawena. "Hawaiian Folkways of Posture and Body Molding." In *Early Hawaiians: An Initial Study of Skeletal Remains from Mokapu, O'ahu,* by C.E. Snow. Lexington: University Press of Kentucky, 1974.

Pukui, Mary Kawena, E.W. Haertig, and Catherine A. Lee. *Nana I Ke Kumu (Look to the Source),* Vol. 1 & 2. Honolulu: Queen Lili'uokalani Children's Center, 1972.

Richards, Butch. Presentation at Hawaiian Lomilomi Association Conference, September 16, 2005.

Silva, Dane Kaohelani. "Hawaii's Healing Tradition." *Massage Magazine,* July/August 2000, p. 89.

"The Lomi Lomi." *Paradise of the Pacific,* July 1892, p. 6.

Twombly, Alexander S. *Hawaii and Its People: The Land of Rainbow and Palm.* Boston: Silver, Burdett and Company, 1900, p. 308.

Photography
Credits

Mahalo for
Their Kōkua

Mahalo to our family and friends whose kōkua, prayers and blessings made this book possible. Some are in the pictures on these pages. Some posed for pictures we were unable to use. Some gave us permission, helped move equipment, or cheered us on. To all of them, we say mahalo!

Kathleen Alvarez, L.M.T.
Patricia Lei Anderson-Ruiz
Valerie Au
Kekuni Blaisdell, M.D.
Mark Chai
Keola Chan
Mary Church
Ron Cox
Mami Cunningham
Michael Cunningham
Dewit Emanuel
Lauren Franzwa
M. J. Harden
Hekili Hiraga-Kaiahua
Lucia Tarallo Jensen

Natalie Mahina Jensen
Nancy Kahalewai
Yvonne Kaiahua
Kaimana Kāne
Keanu Kāne
Leimomi Kāne
Miwako Kaneakua
Liz Lalo'ulu
Pali Jae Lee
Jimmy Lewis
Queen Lili'uokalani Trust
James M. Maluhia La Pierre
Michelle Medeiros
Sandy Mew-McRoberts
Martha Noyes
Helen O'Connor
Sheila O'Malley
Shelle Silva
Cameron Smith
David Keoni Virden
Makana Wright
Pi'ilani Wright, L.M.T.

Hawaiian Massage : Lomilomi
Sacred Touch of Aloha

. . . .

HOW TO GET MORE LOMILOMI

Do you want to deepen your
understanding about lomilomi
and Hawaiian traditions?

Get Makana Risser Chai's Bishop
Museum book, *Nā Moʻolelo Lomilomi,*
and John Kalani Zak's award-winning
films on DVD, "Hawaiian Healing,"
"Hawaiian Meditations," and
"Pule Wailele."

Would you like to gift this book to
someone you know? Order your
autographed copies today.

Find out more at
www.LomilomiBook.com

. . . .